THE NON-ELECTRIC LIGHTING SERIES

BOOK 3: *Lamp Fuels*

Text & Photos by Ron Brown
Cover by FK
Copyright © 2014 Ronald B. Brown
All rights reserved.
ISBN 978-0-9905564-0-4

R&C Publishing

Newark Valley, New York

Notice: This booklet is designed to provide information on lamp and lantern fuels – hydrocarbons such as kerosene, white gas, mineral spirits, diesel fuel and the like.

It is not the purpose of this guide to reprint all the information that is otherwise available, but to complement, amplify, and supplement other texts and resources. You are urged to read all the available material and learn as much as you can about petroleum lamp fuels and to tailor the information to your specific circumstances.

Every effort has been made to make this guide as complete and accurate as possible. However, there may be mistakes, both typographical and in content. Therefore this text should be used only as a general guide and not as the ultimate source of petroleum lamp-fuel information. Furthermore, this guide contains information that is current only up to the printing date.

The purpose of this manual is to educate and entertain. The views, opinions, positions, of strategies expressed by the author are his alone. The author makes no representations as to the accuracy, completeness, correctness, suitability, or validity of any information in this book and will not be liable for any errors, omissions, or delays in this information or any losses, injuries, or damages arising from its use.

ISBN 978-0-9905564-0-4

Published by R&C Publishing
15 Dr. Knapp Road South
Newark Valley, NY 13811

Printed in the United States of America

Table of Contents

Foreword

An early draft of this book, as the author notes, was reviewed by two petrochemical engineers, a college physics professor, and a chemical engineer. As it so happens, I am the physics professor in question. But that was my past career. Today I work in the oil and gas industry and have been in the industry for almost 20 years.

I want to assure the reader that the information presented in this book is accurate. The topics, written from a lamp-fuel and lantern-fuel point of view, have been simplified but with full confidence I can state that what is presented is correct.

Recall, if you will, the first conversation you had with your child about "the birds and the bees." What kind of conversation was it? Did you use complicated words? Or did you simplify the information and use the simplest language you could think of. Making it simple did not make it less true.

You can earn a college degree on the topic of petroleum. And you could work in the field and continue learning about petroleum all your life. Would you know more than what's in this book? Of course, yes!! But would additional knowledge make what's in this book less true? Definitely not!

Do you know the difference between white gas and white spirits? What about the difference between white spirits and mineral spirits? (Of course, there's always mineral spirits and alcoholic spirits.) How about the difference between mineral oil and mineral spirits? Or coal oil and kerosene?

If you don't have a clear understanding of petroleum products, it's worth spending an evening or two brushing up on the topic. What you'll discover in this book is clear, simple, and straight-forward information. It will be time well spent.

There's a lot of information that you can find on the internet surrounding these topics. Some is just opinion and some is factual. Some makes me laugh, some makes my head shake in disbelief, and some, at times, makes me sad.

Please don't burn your house down. Please don't risk the lives of your family. Please take the time to read these few pages. Please, please, please. READ THE BOOK.

Ester S. Adkisson
Dallas, Texas
June 2014

"Let there be light." (Genesis 1:3)

So Let's Get Started

As soon as we graduate from candles and olive oil to kerosene, the door opens onto the crazy world of bad Internet information about lamp and lantern fuels. Well, not all bad. Probably no more than 50% is silly, misinformed, or dangerous.

But how do you know that you're on the safe side of the road and not the stupid side? That's the purpose of this book. To keep you on the safe side.

Just so you know, a draft of this book was reviewed by a college physics professor, two petrochemical engineers working in the Texas oil patch, and a chemical engineer working in the oil industry in Qatar.

So does that make this book perfect? No. Nothing in life is perfect. But it's pretty good. And you have to start someplace. It is my intent that the info in this book will help keep you safe.

❧❧❧❧❧❧

Did you know that the "cooking gas" in the tank out behind your house is propane – exactly the same as the propane you buy in small cylinders for your Bernz-O-Matic soldering torch?

Did you know that butane, the fuel in your cigarette lighter, turns from gas to liquid at approximately the freezing point of water? As it must be in the gaseous state for ignition to take place, if you remove your lighter from your warm pants pocket in January and lay it on the back porch, in a few minutes it won't light (at least here in New York State).

9

Did you know that jet fuel is kerosene? And that paint thinner and charcoal lighter fluid are both mineral spirits? And that baby oil and brake fluid are both mineral oil . . . the same as the laxative we call "mineral oil" from the drug store?

No? You didn't know? Gee. Maybe this book does have something to offer.

✁✂✃✄✁✂

Crude oil. Crude oil is the stuff that gets pumped out of the ground. It's not at all like the motor oil you put in your automobile engine. The word "oil" is about all the two have in common. Crude oil is smelly, stinky stuff. "Tar with a few rocks in it," as my college professor used to say.

Crude oil is refined into a whole range of products from gases (propane, butane) to liquids (gasoline, kerosene) to solids (paraffin wax).

All of these products are hydrocarbons. The "hydro" part of the word stands for hydrogen. The "carbon" part of the word stands for carbon.

For example, C_3H_8 stands for 3 parts carbon and 8 parts hydrogen and is the chemical formula for propane. For our purposes, we'll discuss just the "C" part. At the price of oversimplification, we'll ignore the hydrogen part, the "H" part.

✁✂✃✄✁✂

To understand oil refining, it helps to understand the process of distilling. A moonshiner's whiskey still – short for distillery – is a good place to start.

The moonshiner starts out with mash – a wine of sorts, with low alcoholic content, created by fermentation. The

10

moonshiner wants to isolate and capture and concentrate the alcohol. He accomplishes this by distilling the mash.

Water boils at 212° F. If you boil some water on the stove, the vapor given off will condense on any surface that is below 212° F – the pan cover, for example – and turn back into a liquid.

Alcohol boils at 173° F. So if the moonshiner heats his mash to above 173° but holds it below 212°, the alcohol will boil off and·leave the water behind. Then if he passes the alcohol vapor over a cold surface it will condense and drip into a Mason jar . . .

As Luke Bryon's country-western song has it:

"Rain makes corn, corn makes whiskey.
"Whiskey makes my baby get a little frisky.
"Rain is a good thang . . ."

We digress. Oil refining is a two-stage affair. First, distillation breaks or fractures the crude oil into groups of hydrocarbons with similar boiling points. The five major fractions are (1) refinery gases, (2) gasoline, (3) kerosene, (4) diesel oil, and (5) residues.

After fractional distillation comes cracking. The world's thirst for gasoline is bigger than fractional distillation can satisfy. Hence the need for cracking – thermal decomposition wherein big molecules of heavy oil are broken down into smaller molecules by heating them as they pass over a catalyst.

We need to be somewhat vigilant in our terminology. "Gas" can be interpreted to mean [1] gasoline (petrol to the British), or it can mean [2] natural gas (methane), or it can mean [3] a vapor (as in the three states of matter – solid, liquid, and gas), or it can be [4] a euphemism for farting (he passed gas). As we go along I'll do my best to differentiate between the various meanings.

Methane (C_1H_4)

One part carbon, four parts hydrogen. Methane is used as a fuel, commonly called natural gas, and is transported via pipeline in LNG form (liquefied natural gas). Methane is also the swamp gas of UFO lore.

Lamps that burn natural gas inside your home, common in the gay '90s – the 1890's – back when "gay" meant happy – are still manufactured. Humphrey, Paulin, and Mr Heater are three U.S. brands. Their use requires that you have a natural gas line into your house. If you heat with natural gas, you do. Lamps burning natural gas are wall-mounted (or ceiling-mounted) and thus not portable.

Ethane (C_2H_6)

Ethane is used as a catalyst in other chemical processes, moreso than as a fuel in and of itself. Note that the carbon number (the carbon-chain or C-number) is climbing (from C_1 to C_2).

Propane (C_3H_8)

I live in the country, beyond the reach of natural gas pipelines. As a consequence, I have a 200 lb. propane tank behind the house. We use propane for cooking.

The company who delivers our gas is Suburban Propane. I can drive to their storefront and refill a small 20 lb. cylinder to use on a camper or RV (recreational vehicle). The tank behind my house and the 20 lb. cylinder contain exactly the same stuff – LPG (liquefied petroleum gas).

The skinny little propane cylinders (400 grams or 14.1 oz.) sold for soldering torches also contain LPG. As do the more squat 465-gram cylinders (16.4 oz.) sold for camping stoves and lanterns. It's all the same stuff – C_3H_8.

Can you hook up a propane camping lantern to a 20 lb. propane tank? Sure. The fittings and extension hoses to do so are sold as a kit under the Century brand name. And also under the Coleman brand name. I bought one myself in the camping section at Walmart.

Propane gas lamps are often employed in cottages and hunting camps located at a distance from both electricity and in-town natural gas lines. These lamps burn LPG (liquefied petroleum gas) rather than LNG (liquefied natural gas).

LPG and LNG lamps can look identical on the outside but propane is more highly pressurized. Propane lamps therefore use a nozzle with a smaller orifice (the hole through which the gas comes) than do natural gas lamps. If you move from city to country, or vice-versa, your gas clothes dryer presents exactly the same orifice problem. Fortunately, conversion kits are readily available.

Butane (C₄H₁₀)

Note we are still climbing the C-numbers.

Butane is used in cigarette lighters and in pressurized cans for one-burner stoves. It turns from a gas to a liquid at 31° F (almost the same as the freezing point of water).

In Mexico (a warm climate), a high percentage of butane is mixed with propane for cooking gas. Butane is sometimes called Mexican gas (i.e. Mexican cooking gas; not automobile gas). Further north, where it's colder, some butane is mixed in with LPG. In Mexico, a lot.

Toronto, Canada, has a large Asian population. In the ethnic food stores, one-burner stoves that run on butane cylinders are very common. The cylinders are lightweight, similar to shaving cream containers. In the USA, these stoves are rare outside restaurant supply stores, although I have seen them at Target.

Butane stoves are easy to light, regulate, and extinguish. Why they are not more popular with the outdoors camping community is no doubt their low-temperature limitations. Ditto for the use of butane in lanterns. Below freezing, a lantern that runs on butane (and there are a few) will not light.

Up to this point we've been talking about gases – methane, ethane, propane, and butane. Each one has a higher carbon-chain or C-number than the one before it. Now let us enter the wonderful world of liquids . . .

Gasoline (C_5 to C_{12})

Here's where things take an ugly turn. My underlying theme is that a hierarchy of petroleum products exists, ranging from C_1 (swamp gas) to C_{25} (solid wax). As the C-number gets higher, the viscosity or "glueyness" increases.

But as soon as we leave the gases and go to the liquids, the C-number becomes a range (e.g. C_5 to C_{12}) rather than a single numeral (C_5). And the ranges overlap. And, if we go poking around, we discover that various authorities disagree on how the ranges should be defined.

Unfortunately, unless we delve into a study of alkanes, alkenes, alkynes, dienes, homolytic fission, C-C scission, and disproportionation, we'll have to live with our somewhat simplified view of things.

Gasoline, if you remember, is a major "fraction" from fractional distillation at the refinery. As such, "gasoline" is an all-inclusive term for everything between the refined gasses (discussed above) and kerosene. Our interest here is in fuel for lamps and lanterns. A look back at history is probably the easiest way to clarify things.

17

In 1859 oil was successfully drilled in Titusville (TEE-tus-vil), Pennsylvania. But the first Model "T" Ford didn't roll off the assembly line for another 49 years – September 27, 1908, to be exact. So the crude oil that Standard Oil pumped for half a century . . . where was it used? Answer. In kerosene for lighting, not gasoline for driving.

The gasoline used in early cars was "white gas" – so named because it was as clear as water. White gas was simply gasoline without additives. Today, the "regular" gas you buy at the pump (with additives) is 87 octane. Old-time white gas was only 50 octane.

As automobile engines evolved, white gas turned out to have a major drawback. It would spontaneously ignite under relatively low compression. To better visualize the problem, let's construct an imaginary automobile engine –

Tennis balls come three-in-a-tube. We remove two. The tube is a cylinder. The one ball remaining inside is a piston. We install a spark plug in one end. A little valve beside the spark plug opens and a volatile mixture of gasoline and air is injected. The piston travels towards the spark plug, compressing the fuel/air mix. This is called the compression stroke.

When the ball nears the spark plug, a spark is triggered, igniting the fuel/air mix. The "explosion" drives the ball, the piston, to the other end of the tube. This is called the power stroke. Repeated power strokes are what turn the wheels of your car.

It's the compression stroke that gives the problem. As the fuel/air mix is compressed, it gets hot. In a diesel engine the compression ratio reaches 20:1 and the fuel/air mixture gets so hot it ignites spontaneously. It does not even need a spark plug.

But in a gasoline engine the compression ratio is much lower. In a Model "T" Ford it was only 4.5:1 – and white gas worked fine. Could you have driven your Tin Lizzie on Coleman fuel? Absolutely. Could you do it today? Drive your car on Coleman fuel? Absolutely not. Automobile engines have changed. Today you need 87 octane, not 50.

In time, starting from Model "T" days, a distribution system for gasoline evolved. The early gas pumps dispensed 50-octane white gas. And that was what Coleman lanterns burned. Both cars and lanterns used white gas.

Eventually, white gas became obsolete for automobile use.

The Model "A" Ford was introduced in 1927. A special after-market head was produced in 1930 that gave a 5.22:1 compression ratio. It was only available for use on police cars. But technology moves fast and by World War II automobile compression ratios of 6:1 and 8:1 were common.

At the higher ratios, white gas would detonate during the compression stroke, before the spark plug ever had a chance to set it off. A distinctive knocking sound resulted. If bad enough, it would blow a hole in the cylinder wall.

Higher-octane gas resisted detonation due to compression. Lead (i.e. tetraethyl lead) was added to gasoline to raise its effective octane level. Regular gas had some lead; hi-test had more. If a high-compression engine requiring hi-test gas was run on regular, it knocked.

So what the heck is octane?

Fair question. Methane, if you remember from the discussion above, has one carbon atom. Ethane has two. Propane, three. Butane, four. Pentane, five. Hexane, six. Heptane, seven. And octane, eight.

By definition, the octane number of an octane/heptane blend is the percentage of octane in that blend.

If heptane is compressed just a small amount, it ignites spontaneously. But octane can be compressed a lot with no ignition.

So, gasoline rated as "87 octane" contains 87% octane and 13% heptane **OR** it contains ingredients that produce anti-knock effects equivalent to 87% octane and 13% heptane.

❧❧❧❧❧

Back to our story. Long before World War II, gas stations were pumping leaded gas (dyed red so that customers wouldn't get it mixed up with white gas). To make itself even more distinctive, Sunoco introduced Blue Sunoco. In Junior High, I pumped Blue Sunoco at my uncle's gas station. Red, white, and blue. Patriotic, eh?

White gas became harder and harder to find. But Coleman lanterns still needed it; leaded gas would clog a lantern's generator (see Glossary) and the byproducts of combustion were not healthy to breathe. So Coleman began selling "Coleman fuel" – white gas sold under a brand name. Lantern owners began lugging home cans of Coleman fuel just as the earliest automobile owners lugged home cans of white gas.

Coleman took pains to establish their product as different from (and superior to) white gas at the pump. To make the distinction visceral, Coleman fuel got a splash of green dye and a higher price tag.

It is well to remember that Coleman lanterns were not designed to run on Coleman fuel. Coleman lanterns existed forty years before Coleman fuel existed. Coleman lanterns were designed to run on white gas.

Today, white gas no longer exists at the pump (unless you live in Amish country). With the competition gone, Coleman's position has mellowed –

> "What type of fuel is right for you?
> "Coleman® Fuel
> "Also called white gas or camping fuel . . ."
> © 2010 The Coleman Company, Inc.
> http://www.coleman.com/coleman/colemancom/choo
> se_fuel.asp

Leaded gas replaced white gas for automobile use but leaded gas poisoned people and was itself replaced by unleaded in the 1970's. Unleaded didn't mean zero additives, however. Unleaded meant different additives. Non-lead additives. The knock problem still had to be addressed. No additives would translate to 50-octane gasoline.

For my generation, I think a lot of confusion about "white gas" originated with Amoco, the brand of gasoline sold by the American Oil Company. (The Amoco brand is no longer sold, incidentally.) Amoco was a lead-free gas that used aromatics (beyond the scope of this discussion) rather than tetraethyl lead to increase the octane rating. Amoco was colorless and commonly called white gas by the gas-station owners. That was a misnomer. True white gas was, and is, additive-free. Amoco was not additive-free.

Older Coleman lanterns were designed to run on one fuel, white gas. Newer models are "dual-fuel" and designed to run on either white gas or unleaded petrol. But even unleaded gas gums up a lantern's generator. The choice of which fuel to use comes down to a gallon of petrol for $4 plus an occasional $12 replacement generator or $12 for a gallon of Coleman fuel.

Back in the heyday of lanterns, incidentally, "dual-fuel" meant white gas and kerosene. Today it means white gas and automobile gas. (There will be more on this in The Non-Electric Lighting Series when we get to the topic of pressure lanterns.)

We've pretty well beaten the topic of white gas to death but I'd like to add a personal anecdote about storing it.

An elderly neighbor once gave me several gallons of Coleman fuel. His children were grown and gone and he was no longer the avid camper he once was. I would guess that the cans he set on my back porch had been stored in his garage some twenty years. The tops were speckled with rust.

All the cans were brand new when placed in storage. When I received them, still unopened, some were half empty. The factory-installed metal seals under the caps were intact. But summer heat had pressurized the contents and forced the gas past the seals.

Could my neighbor have stopped those minute leaks with paint or wax? I seriously doubt it. Only shielding the container from heat would have prevented the leaks.

Mineral Spirits (C_7 to C_{12})

Outside the United States, "mineral spirits" is often called white spirits. The term white gas, discussed in the previous section, is sometimes confused with white spirits.

Mineral spirits is on the borderline between gasoline and kerosene. So to understand it we must understand a bit more about both gasoline and kerosene – even though we haven't discussed kerosene quite yet.

Gasoline is "flammable" whereas kerosene is "combustible." Here's an interesting little experiment you can perform yourself to illustrate the difference. Just be careful of your eyebrows.

Clamp a metal teaspoon in a vise (bowl facing up). Using an eyedropper, fill the spoon with some gasoline. You can use either white gas (i.e. Coleman fuel) or automobile gas (i.e. petrol) – they both react the same. Light a wooden kitchen match. Bring the flame near the spoon. When the match-flame is ¼-inch away from the spoon the gas will burst into flame.

(Be careful how you extinguish the flame. If you blow on it really hard, you can successfully scatter burning droplets of gasoline all over your workbench. Trust me.)

Now try the same experiment with kerosene. The kero will not ignite even when the edge of the flame touches the spoon. Nor will it ignite for the length of time it takes the match to burn down.

So that's the demonstrable difference between gasoline (flammable) and kerosene (combustible). Where do you think mineral spirits fits in?

Answer. Mineral spirits is combustible. Like kerosene, it will not light.

Now this is a good example of how confusing things can be. Having just said that both petrol and white gas are flammable, we look at a gallon of Coleman fuel (white gas) and it says, **"Fuel/Combustible."** It does not say flammable. It says combustible. Geez Louise. Where did we go wrong?

We didn't. Coleman is not using "combustible" as an adjective to describe fuel. Their container is simply bilingual. *Combustible* is a noun; it's the Spanish word for fuel.

❧❦❧❦❧❦❧

OSHA defines a combustible liquid as "any liquid having a flash point at or above 100° F."

"Flash point" is the lowest temperature at which a liquid can form an ignitable mixture in air. A flammable liquid has a flash point below 100° F.

White gas has a flash point below 100° F. Well below. Ditto for petrol. The flash point for white gas is –40° F while gasoline is –45° F. They are both flammable.

Most people think that combustible sounds more dangerous than flammable; that a combustible liquid takes fire more easily. And the opposite is true. So I composed a limerick to help you remember:

> There once was a flammable female
> Who wed a combustible guy.
> She'd burst into flame
> While he remained tame.
> It sometimes made both of them cry.

ᴕᵍᐁ ᐁᵍᐁ ᐁᵍᐁ

But here's the point. At room temperature (below 100° F), gasoline evaporates. That means it gives off gaseous, ignitable fumes at all times. If you poured an ordinary kerosene lamp full of gasoline, it would not only give off gaseous fumes at the top of the wick, it would give off gaseous fumes inside the fuel tank as well. With an open flame at the wick only a few inches away from the gas fumes in the tank, you would have a Molotov cocktail on your hands. Gasoline at room temperature is flammable. Please don't use it in a kerosene lamp.

Kerosene does not evaporate fast enough at room temperature to form an ignitable mixture in air. That's why you couldn't light it with a match in our little experiment. If you pour a kerosene lamp full of kerosene, it doesn't evaporate and produce fumes inside the fuel tank. Even at the top of the wick, you must preheat the kerosene (with a match) before it will turn to a gaseous state and ignite. Kerosene will burn, not at room temperature where it is a liquid, but at an elevated temperature where it turns into a gas. Kerosene is termed combustible.

And mineral spirits, like kerosene, is also combustible. MSDS sheets for seven different brands of mineral spirits – Sunnyside, RustOleum, Klean-Strip, Parks, Sherwin Williams, Kerr, and Ace (Barr) – show flash points ranging from 102° F to 109° F. The lowest is Sunnyside; the highest, Kerr.

MSDS sheets for five different brands of **odorless** mineral spirits – Sunnyside, RustOleum, Klean-Strip, Parks, and ConocoPhillips – show flash points from 105° F to 127° F. The lowest is RustOleum; the highest, ConocoPhillips.

Long ago and far away, white gas (highly flammable) was used for stain removal and dry cleaning. In the search for a safer, less volatile agent, the spec for mineral spirits was developed in 1924 by W.J. Stoddard, an Atlanta dry cleaner, and Lloyd E. Jackson of the Mellon Research Institute. Hence, mineral spirits is also known as Stoddard solvent.

Stoddard solvent in dry cleaning was eventually replaced by carbon tetrachloride. That removed the fire hazard completely. Carbon tet was even used in fire extinguishers. But carbon tet was itself banned in 1970 because it caused severe liver damage.

We digress. Back to our discussion . . .

Kerosene (C_{12} to C_{15})
Coal Oil (C_{10} to C_{16})
Jet Fuel (C_{10} to C_{14})

In 1846, Abraham Gesner (in Canada) refined a liquid fuel from coal. He named his product kerosene. It later turned out that kerosene could be produced more easily from petroleum though it continued to be referred to as "coal oil." Kerosene is sometimes spelled kerosine; both spellings are pronounced the same.

In 1848, James Young (in Scotland) derived a similar product from the distillation of cannel coal. Young named his product "paraffine oil" because at low temperatures it congealed and looked like paraffin wax. Young patented his process in 1850. Despite clear priority of discovery, Gesner did not obtain his first kerosene patent until 1854.

Note. Cannel coal (rhymes with flannel) is the traditional albeit sloppy pronunciation of "candle coal." Today, cannel coal is classified as a type of oil shale. In the day, it "was prized for fireplaces as an excellent fuel that burned with a bright flame, was easily lit, and left virtually no ash." (Wikipedia)

Just as sugar from sugar beets and sugar from sugar cane are chemically identical, so are kerosene produced from coal (coal oil) and kerosene produced from petroleum. The raw materials are not the same but the end product is.

As mentioned earlier, the production of kerosene for lighting was the main use of crude oil in the late 1800's. Then cars came along, shifting production to gasoline, and the electric light bulb came along rendering kerosene production nearly obsolete . . . until jet planes arrived.

A couple of keroseny things you should be aware of:

The flash point of kerosene ranges from 100° F to 150° F (per the ConocoPhillips MSDS). Civilian jet fuel is essentially kerosene with stricter specifications on smoke point and freeze point. Jet A specification is used in the United States whereas Jet A-1 is the standard specification in the rest of the world. Jet B is a cold-weather blend.

From what I've seen on-line, people who use Jet A (in Kero-Sun heaters and the like) say that it smells really bad, far worse than K-1 kerosene. If you spill Jet A in the back of your camper, for example, the smell "never goes away."

The military has its own nomenclature. The following comes from Wikipedia:

JP-1
JP stands for jet propellant; JP-1 was introduced in 1944; it was a "pure kerosene" fuel, also called AVTUR (AViation TURbine fuel).

JP-2 and JP-3
Alternate jet fuels developed during WWII but now obsolete and no longer used.

JP-4
The primary US Air Force jet fuel 1951-1995. It was a 50/50 mix of kerosene and gasoline. Also called AVTAG (AViation Turbine Gasoline). NATO code F-40. Very similar to civilian Jet B.

JP-5
A yellow kerosene-based jet fuel with a high flash point (140° F), making it safer on aircraft carriers. Also used in turbine engines; alternate names include AVCAT for AViation CArrier Turbine fuel. NATO code F-44.

JP-6
Developed as part of the XB-70 Valkrie program. When XB-70 was cancelled, the JP-6 spec was also cancelled.

JP-7
Used in supersonic aircraft; contains many additives (e.g. a cesium-containing compound that aids in disguising the radar signature of the exhaust plume).

JP-8
Kerosene-based; specified by the U.S. government in 1990 to replace diesel fuel; flash point is 115° F; is today's

primary Air Force jet fuel; replaced JP-4; smells stronger than JP-4. NATO code F-34.

These are military designations, remember, not civilian.

❧❧❧❦❧❧❧

How about this one: "I have a recommendation for those seeking Kerosene. The International Specifications for Kerosene are almost if not exactly the same as commercial Jet-A Fuel . . . Since I market petroleum products in the NW (Seattle-Vancouver, BC and parts of Alaska) I have been purchasing Jet A in bulk and selling it as Kero for years. It works very well . . ." http://fuel.papo-art.com/ [1996]

❧❧❧❦❧❧❧

Next, safety. I started out as an industrial arts teacher. I was taught that all of the high school industrial arts shops in New York State had a red-painted metal can with a spring-loaded cover labeled "oily rags." Why? Because oily rags are subject to spontaneous combustion.

Let me bore you with a story. My mother started a couple of minor house fires over the years (in the winter) by bringing in semi-frozen clothes from the outside clothesline and draping them over the shades of electric lamps. Whereupon she forgot them and they dried out, then ignited, then ignited the lamp shade, etc.

So, when my father, sitting up late one winter's night, smelled something scorching, he did not dismiss it. He got up and went nosing about.

There was a wood cookstove in the kitchen that had years earlier been converted to kerosene. The wall behind the stove was shared by both the kitchen (inside) and the woodshed (outside). There was a barrel of kerosene in the woodshed. A pipe went from the barrel though the wall and to the stove. Next to the stove, a rag hung on the pipe. It was winter. The wall was cold; the pipe was cold; the old stove was no longer in use.

The rag had been used to wipe up occasional smears of kerosene. And it was the rag that was smoldering and smelled scorched. Dad picked it up and immediately dropped it on the floor when it burned his fingers. Then he picked it up with a fork and walked to the back door and flipped it out onto the snowbank. When it went through the door and hit the outside air with the higher oxygen content, it burst into flames.

Now you can rationalize this incident as you will, but the simple truth is that oily rags are subject to spontaneous combustion . . . a fact known to everyone of my grandfather's generation but to no-one of my children's generation. I invite nonbelievers to Google for 'spontaneous combustion oily rags' and do their homework before scoffing.

31

Consider this from back in the day: "Spontaneous combustion [is] . . . the ignition of bodies by the internal development of heat without the application of an external flame. It not infrequently takes place among heaps of rags . . . lubricated with oil . . ." – *Encyclopedia Americana*, 1919

Fuel Oil No. 1 (C_9 to C_{16})
Fuel Oil No. 2 (C_{10} to C_{20})
Diesel Fuel (C_{17} to C_{25})

If you have a mobile home with an oil furnace and an outside fuel tank, then you're likely burning No. 1 fuel oil. If you have a house with a fuel tank in the basement, then you're likely burning No. 2 fuel oil. There are, of course, all kinds of additives and summer-winter blends to confuse things.

The point is that No. 2 fuel oil will turn cloudy at a warmer temperature than No. 1. Then, as the temperature drops, No. 2 will congeal and refuse to flow to your furnace. Not a good thing. No. 2, will work fine, however, if the fuel tank is in your basement, shielded from the cold.

No. 1 fuel oil is very similar if not identical to kerosene. Diesel fuel, on the other hand, starts out as No. 2 fuel oil and then has additives put in (mostly for lubrication). The flash point for diesel fuel ranges from 126° F to 205° F (Wikipedia). In northern states (e.g. Maine), the oil companies add kerosene to diesel fuel in the wintertime to prevent gelling.

We're just now (2014) completing a transition period in the United States. The stink we always associated with kerosene and diesel fuel came from their sulfur content. But the rules have changed.

First, sulfur concentration is expressed in ppm (parts per million). And one part per million is a rather small quantity. Picture one drop of paint thinner, measured out with an eyedropper, spread across 17 gallons of paint. That is one part per million.

There are two grades of kerosene: K-1 (with 400 ppm sulfur) and K-2 (with 3000 ppm sulfur). K-2 kerosene is used in appliances vented to the outside (i.e. that have chimneys). K-1 kerosene is used in appliances that lack venting – Kero-Sun heaters, etc.

Diesel fuel has its own story. As noted above, No. 2 fuel oil and diesel fuel are virtually interchangeable. Houses are heated with No. 2 fuel oil, farm tractors run on diesel fuel, and over-the-road eighteen-wheelers run on diesel fuel.

LOW SULFUR NON-HIGHWAY DIESEL FUEL
(500 ppm Sulfur Maximum)

WARNING
Federal law prohibits use in all model year 2011 and newer non-road engines.

May damage model year 2011 and newer non-road engines.

Federal law prohibits use in highway vehicles of engines.

ULTRA-LOW SULFUR HIGHWAY DIESEL FUEL
(15 ppm Sulfur Maximum)

Required for use in all highway diesel vehicles and engines.

Recommended for use in all diesel vehicles and engines.

Both environmental restrictions and taxes have long favored the homeowner and the farmer over the trucker. Hence, No. 2 fuel oil and off-road diesel (with 5000 ppm sulfur) are cheaper than low-sulfur highway fuel (500 ppm).

Might truckers be tempted to cheat and run their trucks on the less expensive No. 2 fuel oil? Of course. For that reason, red dye is added to the high-sulfur, low-tax stuff so that it can be determined (by sampling the "gas tank") if truckers are breaking the law.

And today, "low sulfur" diesel fuel has been replaced with "ultra-low sulfur" (15 ppm). It means that dirty old diesel fuel now has less smell than K-1 kerosene (400 ppm).

Could the oil companies make 15 ppm kerosene if they wanted to? Yes. Do they? Yes. Kerosene is part of the winter blend of diesel fuel. To have an end product of 15 ppm, the kerosene additive must be 15 ppm as well as the diesel.

Can you buy it? Maybe. Countrymark Cooperative of Mt. Vernon, Indiana, for example, is one company that makes and sells ultra-low sulfur kerosene (15 ppm). But their sales appear to be regional (Kentucky and Indiana).

W.M. Barr has a line of solvents and fuels trademarked Klean-Strip. There is Klean-Strip Stripper (for paint removal); Klean-Strip Klean-Heat; and Klean-Strip Kerosene. (Confusing, yes?) Per its MSDS, Klean-Strip Kerosene contains 10 ppm sulfur and has a flash point of 101° F.

But that's for Klean-Strip *Kerosene*. Klean-Strip *Klean-Heat* is verbally advertised as "odorless" although the sulfur content is not disclosed. The flash point of Klean-Heat is 145° F. Klean-Heat is a "synthetic" product. Synthetics are discussed below.

Mineral Oil (C_{15} and above)

Mineral oil is a petroleum product. You can think of it as liquid Vaseline. You can buy it in the drug store as a laxative. It's also sold as baby oil. And as hydraulic fluid for use in your dump truck. It's used as brake fluid, although today silicone brake fluid has become more common. Just as the Model "T" Ford was originally designed to run on alcohol, diesel engines were originally designed to run on mineral oil. It's thick, viscous stuff. I've successfully used it in vegetable-oil lamps as shown in Book 2 of this series, *Olive Oil Lamps &c.*

Synthetic Products

Kerosene substitutes are introduced from time to time. Their main claim to fame is low odor. They tend to be regional products, not available in all areas or in all stores or at all seasons of the year. One thing is a given – they cost more than kerosene. Two of the most popular are Ultra-Pure lamp oil from Lamplight Farms and Klean-Heat from W.M. Barr.

To some people, the synthetics are the greatest thing since sliced bread. To others, they're an over-priced rip-off. None that I've seen reveal their actual ppm sulfur content, either on their labels or in their MSDS sheets.

There is never total agreement on these things. Aladdin lamps in particular provoke a lot of fuel-related discussion.

The Aladdin Knights, a group of dedicated Aladdin collectors, say, "Other fuels which have been tried successfully are Lamplight Farms 'Ultra Pure' lamp oil…" http://www.aladdinknights.org/faq.php

The Aladdin Mantle Lamp Company recommends against using Ultra-Pure fuel in Aladdins. (Then again, the Aladdin Mantle Lamp Company sells its own competing brand of lamp fuel.)
www.aladdinlamps.com/ViewPage.asp?PageID=2

"I used Ultra-Pure . . . exclusively in all my kero lamps for years [including Aladdin] . . . [Aladdin Mantle Lamp Company's] lack of recommendation is pure BS!" (Fil Graff, Aladdin Knight, The International Guild of Lamp Researchers, question 2442)

Lamplight Farms, the makers of Ultra-Pure, says, "Use Lamplight® Regular lamp oil for your Aladdin lamp. You cannot use Ultra-Pure® as it will cause premature failure of the mantle material."
www.lamplight.com/Consumer/KnowledgeBase.aspx?KnowledgeID=2233

With all the brouhaha I decided a test was in order. So I ran my trusty Aladdin for one full evening on Ultra-Pure ($32/gallon); then for an evening on Klean-Strip Klean-Heat ($11/gallon); then on Klean-Strip Kerosene ($11/gallon); then on Aladdin brand lamp fuel ($19/gallon); then on odorless mineral spirits ($12-18/gallon); and finally on K-1 kerosene (the stuff with the red dye in it) from the local gas station ($4/gallon).

The procedure was to fill and light the lamp outside on the breezeway, let it warm up for 15 minutes on the breezeway, then take it inside and place it in the middle of the dining room table. Hours later, the still-burning lamp was taken back to the breezeway where it was extinguished and allowed to cool. Results? Truth time . . . you could not smell any of them in the house . . . even the cheap stuff with the red dye . . .

You take it from there.

Mineral Spirits Revisited

We need to elaborate the topic of mineral spirits; the Internet absolutely vibrates with bad information.

Grammatically, mineral spirits is used in the singular. CORRECT: Where is the mineral spirits? INCORRECT: Are mineral spirits safe in a kerosene lamp?

But, plural or singular, debating the second question (the safety of mineral spirits in a kerosene lamp) would be, to most of us, on par with watching C-span in a hospital waiting room. Boring, boring, boring.

To a kerosene lamp salesman, however, the mere asking generates an emotional response akin to kicking the crutches out from under his aged grandmother. The screaming gets pretty intense.

Let me give you the answer up front. My answer, that is, the answer that satisfies me. Because you can't prove anything to anybody. You can only prove it to your own satisfaction.

Yes, in my opinion, it is safe to use mineral spirits in a kerosene lamp. I have used mineral spirits in simple, flat-wick lamps and in Dietz's and Duplex's and Rayo's and Kosmos's and B&H's and Aladdin's and Coleman 214's and 237's and 639's and 639C's and Britelyt 150CP's and Petromax 500CP's – all of which are designed specifically for kerosene. And it worked fine in every case, without a hitch.

Granted, just because I did it doesn't mean it's safe. Like crossing the street without looking. Doing it without incident doesn't mean it's safe to do so.

That being said, however, I've actually tested mineral spirits and compared it side-by-side to kerosene, not just read about it or copied over what someone else said. The next two paragraphs summarize my conclusion in non-technical terms:

Picture yourself in the early morning, standing in front of your dresser drawer, picking out socks. You don't want to turn on the light and disturb your wife. Although the light from the window is weak, you have no difficulty distinguishing between the white athletic socks and the black dress socks. But separating the black from the navy blue is more of a challenge.

Now let's say that white gas, highly flammable, is white. And let's say that kerosene is black. So my analogy is this.

White gas is to white socks as kerosene is to black socks. And kerosene is to black socks as mineral spirits is to navy blue.

They really are that close. Now, if that conclusion satisfies you, feel free to skip a few pages. But if you are in the ranks of those sermonizing that mineral spirits equals evil, then this section may cause your ulcer to flare up.

Bad Info

"NO MINERAL SPIRITS in a kerosene lamp! That is NO, none, not ANY!" ::Fil Graff:: Secretary of The International Guild of Lamp Researchers, December 22, 2000, Guild archives (ref. question #976)

Show me some evidence, Fil. Shouting doesn't make it so.

"I'm not even sure what the relationship between 'diesel', 'furnace oil', and 'kerosene' is." ::Fil Graff:: Guild archives, June 9, 2004 (ref. question #2808)

Well, at least that's cleared up.

Before we tackle mineral spirits *per se*, please consider the relationship between gasoline and kerosene.

Gasoline is flammable. That means, by definition, it has a flash point under 100° F. Gasoline evaporates at room temperature. If you splash some on your hand, it feels cool. That's the gasoline evaporating, robbing calories from your skin.

Kerosene is combustible. It has a flash point over 100° F. For all practical purposes, kerosene does not evaporate at room temperature.

Gasoline is not safe in a wick-fed kerosene lamp because gas fumes are being given off at all times (as the gasoline evaporates) and can be ignited by the lamp's flame. Gasoline is safe in a pressure lantern, however, because it's a sealed system. There are no gas fumes floating about at random.

If you drop a match in a bucket of gasoline, it ignites instantly. It "flashes." The entire surface of the gasoline (i.e. all the petrol that is in a gaseous state) ignites simultaneously. (In fact, that's how my dad used to clean out 55-gallon drums. He'd pour in half an inch of gasoline followed by a match. A couple of hours later, the barrel was clean as a whistle. Don't ask me about the ecology or the atmosphere, however.)

But if you drop a match in a bucket of kerosene, it goes out. It does not ignite. There are not enough fumes to be ignited. The match goes "psst" as it disappears beneath the surface, just as it would in a bucket of water.

And where does mineral spirits fit in? Answer. Like kerosene, it will not ignite when you drop a match in the bucket. I've done it. Like kerosene, mineral spirits is "combustible." It is not "flammable."

Just to Clarify

This discussion of mineral spirits deals with mineral spirits, not necessarily "paint thinner."

When I was a young man, we used lead-based house paint and thinned that paint with two things: linseed oil and turpentine. Turpentine was distilled from pine trees. Mineral spirits, made from petroleum, was considered barely good enough to rinse out our paintbrushes.

Then all the pine trees got cut down and turpentine went to $20 per gallon. Suddenly mineral spirits, at $2 per gallon, was considered pretty darn good paint thinner.

Now that mineral spirits is $8-10 and odorless mineral spirits is $12-18, cheaper paint thinners are constantly being introduced. They all appear to contain mineral spirits plus a bunch of other chemicals I can't pronounce. So let me clarify. The subject of my testing here is mineral spirits and mineral spirits only.

■ ABOVE: Here's some paint thinner "<u>with</u> Mineral Spirits." But *how much* mineral spirits? Maybe 1%? Maybe 99%? We don't know and they're not talking. ■

■ **ABOVE:** This paint thinner is 100% mineral spirits. ■

■ **ABOVE:** Perhaps, instead of Sunnyside 100% mineral spirits labeled as paint thinner, you might prefer Sunnyside 100% mineral spirits labeled as mineral spirits. *Say what?* ■

■ **ABOVE:** According to their respective MSDS sheets, Klean-Strip *Kerosene* has 10 ppm sulfur whereas Klean-Strip *Odorless Mineral Spirits* has an "aromatic hydrocarbon-like odor." Its sulfur content is secret. ■

Bad Info

The New York Times reported on October 28, 1990, that, " a barge . . . struck a reef in the Hudson river spilling 163,000 gallons of fuel [kerosene] . . . Coast Guard official Mr. Holmes said . . . that 70 percent of the spill would be gone in 3 days due to the natural evaporation rate of Kerosene."

Not so fast. I checked the evaporation rate of kerosene by pouring some into a saucer and checking its weight at intervals. In 24 hours, 12% had evaporated.

So, if I spill 100 gallons, 24 hours later I'll have 88 gallons remaining (the other 12 gallons having evaporated).

At the end of 48 hours I'll have 77.4 gallons. At the end of 72 hours (3 days) I'll have 68.1 gallons. I started out with a hundred. For me, 68% is pretty good accuracy for my plastic diet scales compared to the 70% figure in the newspaper.

But wait! Somebody got their reciprocal discombobulated from their complement. Because it's only 30% that's evaporated in 3 days and 70% that remains in the water. Not 70% that will be gone.

But who am I to disagree with the New York Times and the U.S. Coast Guard?

Evaporation Rates

In weather reporting, rain gauges at remote locations have the problem of water evaporating between the time it rains and when the gauge is read. To suppress water evaporation, a tiny bit of kerosene is put in the rain gauge. It floats on top of the water and prevents the water from evaporating so as to give an accurate reading. The point? The evaporation rate of the kerosene is s-l-o-w. But how about mineral spirits?

Evaporation rate is hard to find but we know it has an inverse relationship to boiling point (i.e. the lower the temperature at which something boils, the faster it's evaporating). Sunnyside (brand) mineral spirits has a boiling point ranging from 300° to 400° F. Sunnyside odorless mineral spirits has a boiling point between 354° and 372° F. Sunnyside kerosene, 350°-572° F.

So there's an overlap in the boiling-point range and an overlap in the evaporation-rate range. We conclude that

46

mineral spirits and kero are not identical . . . but are very close.

MSDS Sheets

OSHA (the Occupational and Safety Health Administration) was created in 1970 with the mission of preventing injuries and protecting the health of American workers in the workplace. In the 70's and 80's, OSHA brought MSDS's (Material Safety Data Sheets) into being. They were posted in factory lunchrooms where workers could see, up close and personal, the nature of the chemicals they were being asked to handle. You really can't fault the intent of the law.

But in practice, lawyers and engineers teamed up to produce documents that were, in the name of transparency, gibberish – technical jargon, trade terms, codes, and references to government standards that were themselves incomprehensible. Before MSDS, management didn't want workers to know the dangers so didn't tell them. After MSDS, management still didn't want workers to know the dangers and so buried them in detail.

Germane to our discussion, sometimes an MSDS sheet will specify the actual flash point of the liquid at hand. ConocoPhillips, for example, says the flash point of its odorless mineral spirits is 127° F and Coleman says the flash point of kerosene is 130° F.

That's in contrast to other manufacturers and distributors who merely specify the minimum for the product to qualify as combustible, not the actual flash-point value of the liquid in question. Citco says the flash point of its kerosene is 100° F. Ditto for Hess.

Sometimes you'll see >100° F (the > symbol means greater than). In this case, again, 100° is the specification and the MSDS sheet is merely saying, "We meet or exceed spec for this product." Sometimes you will see the flash point stated as 100.4° F. What's that all about? That's what 38° C converts to. Are we having fun yet?

Test #1 – Fuel Temp. & Flame Temp.

I ran two Rayos side by side for seven hours. One on kerosene; the other on mineral spirits. Before starting, I measured ten different chimneys until I found two that were exactly the same height and diameter. Both lamps had brand new Rayo (brand) wicks, freshly trimmed. When taking the fuel temperature inside the tank, I used an aluminum-foil shield to block the heat between the lamp's chimney and the thermometer.

Side by side at cruising altitude (roughly equivalent to a 40-watt incandescent light bulb), it was easy to keep the two lamps at a similar brightness.

I measured the in-tank fuel temperatures at one-hour intervals. From beginning to end, they were equal. Over seven hours, the kero lamp used 28 fluid ounces of fuel; the mineral spirits lamp used 30 oz.

The other thing I wanted to assess during this test was the flame temperature. It's the glowing carbon particles in a lamp's flame that produce light, that allow you to see the flame. The whiter the light, the hotter the flame. The more orange the light, the cooler the flame.

I asked my wife to judge which flame was whiter; not bigger or brighter but whiter. I asked her to judge with the Rayos and, later on, with the side-by-side flat-wick lamps. Unknown to her was which lamp burned which fuel.

On one test she picked the kero lamp as being the whiter flame. On the other test she picked mineral spirits. It really was that close. Personally, I couldn't see a difference.

At the beginning of the Rayo test, the fuel in both lamps measured 65° F. One hour in, they both measured 80°. At the end of two hours, they reached 87°. At the end of three hours, they both remained at 87°. Then they gradually fell (which surprised me; I thought they had stabilized and would remain constant for the duration). At the end of seven hours they had both dropped to 81° F.

Afterwards, I realized that the environment had changed. I began the test in my garage on a spring afternoon. The room temperature at the start was 65°. Seven hours later, the sun had gone down and the garage had cooled to 55°. That's why the lamps, and the fuel in the lamps, got cooler.

Point is, both fuels were the same temperature under the same conditions.

Test #2 – Fuel Temperature (second test)

I tested two flat-wick lamps (glass fonts or fuel tanks) side by side. Same chimney height. New wicks, ⅞" wide. (These lamps produce light on par with 7½-watt nightlights.) I could not measure the fuel temperature hourly because the fonts lacked filler holes (i.e. the entire burner assembly had to be unscrewed from the lamp to gain access to the font). Fuel temperature at the start, in both lamps, was 65° F. At the end of seven hours, the fuel in both lamps was 67° F. The kero lamp had used 7 oz. of fuel; the mineral spirits lamp, 8 oz.

Test #3 – Viscosity/Permeability

I suspended two virgin wicks from a "clothesline" – one into a dish of kerosene; one into a dish of mineral spirits. Whenever I checked them, both fuels had climbed to an equal height on their respective wicks. At the two-hour mark, both had climbed 10½". That's as high as they got.

The clear liquid fuels could not be seen against the white background of the wicks so I held a piece of paper toweling next to each wick, pressed it gently into the wick, and observed the greasy imprint from the fuel on the toweling.

Test #4 – Flash Point

A simplified open-cup method of comparing flash points:

(A) Metal teaspoon clamped in vise. Twenty drops of fuel, from eyedropper, in spoon. Lit candle held under spoon. Stopwatch. Kerosene boiled away in 1 minute 45 seconds. It did not burst into flame. Mineral spirits boiled away in 1 minute 22 seconds. It did not burst into flame.

(B) Twenty drops in metal spoon at room temperature. No candle. Brought match flame sideways to edge of spoon. Kerosene did not ignite. Mineral spirits did not ignite.

(C) Twenty drops in metal spoon. Stopwatch. Candle held under spoon for *5 seconds*. Brought match flame sideways to edge of spoon. Kerosene did not ignite. Mineral spirits did not ignite. Then lowered the match flame vertically into the pool of fuel. Kerosene did not ignite. Mineral spirits did not ignite.

(D) Twenty drops in metal spoon. Stopwatch. Candle held under spoon for *15 seconds*. Brought match flame sideways to edge of spoon. Kerosene ignited. Mineral spirits ignited.

(E) Twenty drops in metal spoon. Stopwatch. Candle held under spoon for *10 seconds*. Brought match flame sideways to edge of spoon. Kerosene did not ignite. Mineral spirits did not ignite. Lowered the match flame vertically into the pool of fuel. Kero ignited. Mineral spirits ignited.

My conclusion: Mineral spirits and kerosene are similar enough to be safely interchangeable in simple flat-wick lamps.

Cruisers Forum

Cruising Boats, Cruising People, Cruising Answers
http://www.cruisersforum.com/forums/f91/lamp-oil-vs-kerosene-23215.html

NOTE: We are still on the topic of mineral spirits here.

QUESTION:
On 1/30/2009, *carbo sailor* asked, "I've got a couple of very nice oil lamps that were just overhauled and refinished. The fellow that did the refinishing suggested that I use kerosene rather than the commercial lamp oil . . . I thus appeal to the forum for some input . . ."

Following are some of the answers *carbo sailor* received:

ANSWER from *GreatKetch* 1/30/2009:
"I've used odorless paint thinner in my lamps for years."
FOLLOWUP from *GreatKetch* 2/1/2009:
"I did ten years of industrial research on chemical and chemical process safety, I really do know of which I speak on this topic."

ANSWER from *roverhi* 1/30/2009:
"I've always used Paint thinner in my Kerosene stoves and lamps. That was using a kerosene stove and 3+ wall lamps with nary a problem in 4 years of living aboard and cruising."

ANSWER from *seacap* 2/1/2009:

"I sailed a 22' boat for 16 years with no engine. Used kerosene lamps all the time . . . Always used kerosene, but mineral spirits will work also."

ANSWER from *rebel heart* 3/1/2009:
"I switched out to mineral spirits in my lamps . . . I already need mineral spirits for certain jobs so I don't need to lug around an additional fuel."

ANSWER from *Icetug* 5/5/2009:
"Low odor mineral spirits work well in wick lamps . . ."

ANSWER from *sarafina* 9/13/2009:
"ace hardware low odor mineral spirits.
12.99 a gallon. burns clean and bright with no unpleasant smell."

ANSWER from *AnsleyS* 9/14/2009:
"We use charcoal lighter fluid for our lamps. It has no smell and is very inexpensive."

EDITORIAL COMMENT
The remarks above are from folks who cruise the Caribbean having yachts of fun while I tinker with old lamps in the basement and fret about Armageddon. But if *carbo sailor* had made his initial inquiry to Fil Graff at The International Guild of Lamp Researchers, he would have received somewhat different advice, eh?

Bad Info

A visit to Woody Kirkman's e-store, *W.T. Kirkman, Oil and Electric Lanterns*, reveals that mineral spirits is a hot-button topic. Woody starts out with **anecdotal evidence**:

"I [*this is Woody speaking*] received an e-mail from a customer that thought it was OK to use paint thinner, despite our warning:

" '. . . I look up and the flame is so high that it burnt the rope ,fell from the tree ,shattered and the ground and lantern were on fire . . . The next night I set the second one on a flat tree stump. Every thing seems fine . . . Next thing I know this one is on fire and the glass also breaks and I'm scrambling to throw dirt on it. The third night I try again. . . This lantern does the same thing.' " [sic]

The problem with anecdotal evidence is that we don't really know what happened and never will. Was this fellow using somebody's chainsaw gas stored in a mineral spirits can? We'll never know.

I suspect the story has merit. But I also suspect that it was the lantern at fault. Perhaps the wick was too narrow. Or the heat shield was missing. Or there was a badly formed seam in the wick tube. Every one of those conditions would have produced the observed results.

(Note the picture on the front cover of this book, lower right-hand side. It shows a flame following a crack in a wick tube – a very dangerous situation! And a *lamp* problem, not a fuel problem.)

Woody gives no indication that he personally saw any of the lanterns or smelled the fuel. And he has a ***conflict of interest***. Sight unseen, given that he sells lanterns, would you expect him to blame the lantern or the fuel?

Woody makes an ***appeal to authority*** – Tony Batts, General Manager of Aladdin Mantle Lamp Company:

"Woody,

"You are most correct, we would never recommend the use of mineral spirits or paint thinner in Aladdin lamps, lanterns, or any flat wick lamps..."

Another **conflict of interest**. What would you expect Tony to say?

"Woody,

"I'm sorry but you are dead wrong. Yes, we sell Aladdin Lamp Fuel at $19 per gallon but odorless mineral spirits for $12 is every bit as good..."

❧❧❧❧❧❧

There are no lobbies, no financial interests, promoting mineral spirits as lamp fuel. That means anyone who sells a competing product can condemn mineral spirits – to the point of making some rather absurd accusations – without fear of contradiction. Other sellers of other lamp fuels, with their own vested interests, remain silent in the victim's defense.

The flash point of kerosene ranges from 100° F to 150° F (per the Phillips 66 MSDS #682950 that you can view on-line: http://www.coastoil.com/MSDS/Phillips%2066%20(Conoco)/Kerosene.pdf).

The flash point of mineral spirits ranges from 102° F to 109° F. The flash point of odorless mineral spirits ranges from 105° F to 127° F. See details in the section above entitled *Mineral Spirits (C_7 to C_{12})*.

Hey! Did you catch it? Mineral spirits qualifies as kerosene.

Afterword

So far, on the lighting theme, I've published:

Lanterns, Lamps & Candles: A User's Guide – a CD in PDF format available from http://www.rc-publishing.com/. *Lanterns* is comprehensive: 70,000 words, 442 pictures.

The Amazing 2000-Hour Flashlight – available both as a Kindle ebook and in paperback from Amazon.

Book 1: Candles (from The Non-Electric Lighting Series) – available both as a Kindle ebook and in paperback from Amazon.

Book 2: Olive Oil Lamps &c. (from The Non-Electric Lighting Series) – available both as a Kindle ebook and in paperback from Amazon.

Book 3: Lamp Fuels (from The Non-Electric Lighting Series) – available both as a Kindle ebook and in paperback from Amazon.

The Non-Electric Lighting Series will be 8-10 books when complete, available as both Kindle ebooks and paperbacks. The series will cover Rayos, Aladdins, Duplexes, Colemans, Petromaxes and lots more. Coming soon to an Amazon near you.

There's also a YouTube video that may be of interest, "Converting a Gas Lantern to Kerosene" (by yours truly, of course).

Glossary

Aladdin lamp
A brand of wick-fed mantle lamp that operates on kerosene.

Aladdin lamp fuel
Kerosene, sold by the Aladdin Mantle Lamp Company, branded as *Aladdin Lamp Fuel*. It was formerly branded *Aladdin Lamp Oil*.

Amoco
A brand of gasoline, no longer marketed, sold by the American Oil Company. Often called "white gas" by station owners because it contained no dye, it was not white gas in the sense of being additive-free. White gas was and is 50 octane. Amoco was not 50 octane.

American Camper
A brand of mantle-lamp that runs on canisters of butane.

Autoignition temperature
The lowest temperature at which a substance will spontaneously ignite (in air) without an external source of ignition (spark or open flame).

AWG
Acronym for *American Wire Gauge*; a wire-gauge standard used for nonferrous (e.g. copper) electrical wires; also called the Brown & Sharpe wire gauge.

Benzin
German word for gasoline.

Bic
A brand of butane cigarette lighter.

Butane

C_4H_{10} A refinery gas; a petroleum product. Propane has three carbon atoms. Butane has four. Gasoline has five or more. Butane is the fuel in Bic-type cigarette lighters.

C

Abbreviation for Celsius.

Carbon monoxide

A colorless, odorless, highly poisonous gas produced by the incomplete combustion of carbon.

Celsius

A temperature scale named after Anders Celsius. The freezing point of water = $0°$ C. The boiling point of water = $100°$ C.

Centigrade

The former name for a temperature scale. From the Latin *centum* (100) and *gradus* (steps). Now called Celsius.

Charcoal lighter fluid

Fluid used to facilitate lighting of charcoal briquettes on a charcoal grill; generically, charcoal lighter fluid is mineral spirits.

Coal oil

The name given to kerosene when it was extracted from coal. The name lived on after petroleum became the raw material from which kerosene was extracted.

Coleman

A USA-based company that makes pressurized mantle lanterns.

Coleman fuel

White gas sold under the Coleman brand name.

Col-Max
A Petromax clone, first manufactured before World War II by Coleman, intended to compete with Petromax in international markets.

Combustible
(1) An adjective used to describe a liquid fuel. Per OSHA, a "combustible" liquid has a flash point at or above 100° F.
(2) The Spanish word (a noun) for fuel.

Crude oil
Unrefined petroleum as it is pumped out of the ground.

Diesel fuel
Diesel fuel is burned in diesel engines and is equivalent to No. 2 fuel oil for home heating. Wick-type kerosene lamps will run on diesel (typically with reduced light output). Only a few pressure lanterns (Petromax being one) will run on diesel.

Distillation
The process of purifying a liquid by boiling it and condensing its vapors.

Drygas
A gasoline additive made from alcohol. "Drygas" is actually a brand name owned by Cristy. Heet is another popular brand. Most drygases are methanol.

Dual Fuel
A term applied to lanterns that burn more than one kind of fuel. The fuels in question were traditionally white gas and kerosene. Coleman's new Dual Fuel label refers to white gas and automobile gas. The new term is disingenuous because older Coleman lanterns designed for white gas will

also burn – safely – unleaded automobile gas and are just as much dual-fuel as the Dual Fuel.

e.g.
Abbreviation for Latin *exempli gratia* meaning "for example."

et al.
Abbreviation for Latin *et alii* meaning "and others."

Ethane
C_2H_6 A refinery gas; a petroleum product. Methane (natural gas) has one carbon atom. Ethane has two. Propane has three.

F
Abbreviation for Fahrenheit.

Fahrenheit
A temperature scale named after Daniel Fahrenheit. The freezing point of water = 32° F. The boiling point of water = 212° F.

Falks
A Canadian brand of wall-mounted mantle-lamps that burn natural gas.

Flammable
An adjective used to describe a liquid fuel. Per OSHA, a "flammable" liquid has a flash point below 100° F.

Flash point
The lowest temperature at which a fuel will ignite in air. Gasoline, for example, evaporates fast enough to produce vapors sufficient to ignite even in sub-zero temperatures. Kerosene, in contrast, does not. Kerosene must be heated to

100° F (or more, depending on brand) before sufficient vapors are produced to take fire.

Font/Fount
A font is the tank on a lamp or lantern that holds fuel. An alternate spelling is fount. The term derives, I believe, from a baptismal fount, the vessel that holds water. (In the context of lighting, the term "font" has nothing to do with typeface or print style.)

Fuel Oil No. 1
In freeze point, flash point, and so on, Fuel Oil No. 1 equates to kerosene and is used by homeowners with fuel tanks located outside. In the winter, thin No. 1 will flow to the furnace when thicker No. 2 would gel. The major difference between Fuel Oil No. 1 and kerosene is the sulfur content. The fuel oil has a higher sulfur content is smellier stuff.

Fuel Oil No. 2
In freeze point, flash point, and so on, Fuel Oil No. 2 equates to diesel fuel and is used by homeowners with fuel tanks located in their basements or underground. Because the fuel is shielded from the cold, Fuel Oil #1 is not necessary. The major difference between Fuel Oil No. 2 and diesel fuel is the sulfur content. The fuel oil has a higher sulfur content and is smellier stuff.

Gas
(1) Short for gasoline. "My car uses high-test gas."
(2) Short for natural gas (methane). "I cook with gas."
(3) One of the three states of matter: solid, liquid, and gas.
(4) Euphemism for farting. "He passed gas."

Gas mantles
One name by which incandescent lantern mantles are known. The "gas" part of the name refers to natural gas, a major fuel in early street lighting.

Gasoline
The distillate fraction of petroleum that lies between butane and kerosene. Gasoline is *flammable*. In America, gasoline (a.k.a. gas) is the fuel used in automobiles. Gasoline to Americans is petrol to the Brits.

Generator
In the context of lanterns, a generator "generates" a gas (of the solid-liquid-gas genre) from a liquid. Liquid fuel enters one end of the generator (a brass tube); heat is applied to the outside of the generator; the liquid inside the generator turns to gas.

Glowmaster
A brand of lamp that uses canisters of butane for fuel.

Heat sink
A passive component that cools a device by absorbing and dissipating heat.

Home heating oil #1
The same as Fuel Oil #1 (q.v.).

Home heating oil #2
The same as Fuel Oil #2 (q.v.).

Humphrey
A brand of wall-mounted gas lamp used with natural gas or propane.

Hydrocarbon
An organic compound that contains only hydrogen and carbon. Petroleum is a hydrocarbon.

Hydrodesulfurization
A catalytic chemical process widely used to remove sulfur from natural gas, gasoline, kerosene, and diesel fuel.

i.e.
Abbreviation for Latin *id est* meaning "that is."

Instant-Lite
A Coleman brand of gas (not kerosene) pressure lantern.

Jet fuel
In general terms, jet fuel equates to kerosene. Jet A is used in the USA and Jet A-1 in the rest of the world. Jet A-1 has a lower freezing point than Jet A plus a mandatory anti-static additive.

JP-8
A US military designation; stands for "Jet Propellant 8." It is kerosene-based and has replaced diesel fuel in government vehicles as well as being used as jet fuel in the Air Force. JP-8 has a strong smell.

K-1 kerosene
Kerosene containing 400 ppm sulfur; for unvented appliances (e.g. Kero-Sun heaters, kerosene lamps).

K-2 kerosene
Kerosene containing 3000 ppm sulfur; for appliances vented to the outside (e.g. furnaces for home heating).

Kerosene
The distillate fraction of petroleum that lies between gasoline and diesel. Kerosene is termed combustible. It has a flash point of 100° F or higher.

Kerosine
An alternate spelling of kerosene.

Klean-Heat
The brand name of a synthetic kerosene substitute. Per its MSDS, the flash point is >145° F.

Lacquer thinner
A flammable solvent used for thinning lacquer (paint). Contains methanol, acetone, toluene, et al.

Lead poisoning
A medical condition caused by increased levels of lead in the body. Lead is toxic. There is no known amount too small not to cause the body harm. Routes of exposure include air, water, soil, food, and consumer products. In the past, burning leaded gas (no longer sold) in a pressure lantern would have contributed to lead poisoning. Today, lead-cored wicks still exist in some in votive candles and will contribute to lead poisoning.

LEL
Acronym for Lower Explosive Limit. It refers to the minimum concentration of vapors that must be present, in air, for ignition to occur.

Lighter fluid
Can refer to either charcoal lighter fluid (combustible) or cigarette lighter fluid (flammable).

LNG
Liquefied Natural Gas (methane).

LP
Acronym for Liquefied Petroleum. (Liquefied petroleum is propane. But the "P" stands for petroleum, not propane.)

LPG
Acronym for Liquefied Petroleum Gas (propane).

Methane
C_1H_4 A refinery gas with one carbon atom. The major component of natural gas.

Mexican gas
Another name for butane (q.v.).

Mineral oil
A thick, viscous petroleum product used for hydraulic fluid, brake fluid, baby oil, laxative, fuel substitute in whale oil lamps, gel candles. Dubbed mineral oil because it is "mineral" as opposed to "vegetable" in origin.

Mineral spirits
a.k.a. Stoddard solvent; a combustible petroleum fuel, originally developed as a dry cleaning agent; very near to kerosene in burning characteristics; used as paint thinner and charcoal lighter fluid.

Mr Heater
A brand of wall-mounted mantle-lamp burning natural gas.

MSDS
Acronym for Material Safety Data Sheet.

MTBE
Acronym for methyl tertiary butyl ether, a gasoline additive.

Naphtha
"A colorless flammable liquid obtained from crude petroleum and used as . . . a raw material for gasoline." – *The American Heritage Dictionary*. Put another way, naphtha is 50-octane white gas. And white gas is one of the raw materials for 87-octane petrol.

Natural gas
A naturally occurring gas mixture consisting primarily of methane. Swamp gas is natural gas.

Neoprene rubber
A synthetic rubber invented by DuPont in 1930. Used in gaskets, hoses, and corrosion-resistant applications due to its chemical inertness.

Nitrile rubber
A synthetic rubber (a.k.a. Buna-N) similar in look and feel to latex. Used in gloves. Resistant to oil, fuel, and other chemicals. Used in the auto and aeronautical industries to make fuel and oil-handling hoses and seals.

Nominal
In drafting and engineering lingo, nominal is a dimension of convenience "for talking purposes." Actual measured dimensions typically vary from nominal.

NorthStar
A brand of lantern sold by Coleman. The NorthStar line includes a liquid-fuel model (for white gas); a propane model; and an electric LED model.

Octane
The octane number of an octane/heptane blend is the percentage of octane in that blend. Gasoline rated "87 octane" contains ingredients that produce anti-knock characteristics equivalent to a blend of 87% octane and 13% heptane.

Odorless mineral spirits
Mineral spirits in which the sulfur content has been reduced by hydrodesulfurization. The sulfur content of odorless mineral spirits is typically <5 ppm.

Orphan
A lamp or lantern for which you cannot buy spare parts; a lamp requiring a part unique to itself.

OSHA
Acronym for Occupational Safety and Health Administration; created in 1970; an agency of the US Department of Labor.

Oxygen starvation
Everything that burns consumes oxygen. If the air/oxygen in your living quarters is depleted, you can suffer oxygen starvation. Short term, you may report "feeling just fine" even though you are pale, confused, have blue lips, and want to sleep. The solution is to open a window and let in some air. Long term (living at high altitude, say), oxygen starvation can result in blindness and heart failure.

Paint thinner
A substance used to thin oil-based house paint (e.g. turpentine, linseed oil, mineral spirits).

Paraffin
(1) In the USA, paraffin is familiar as canning wax (a solid), used to seal jelly jars in home canning.

(2) In the UK, paraffin is the name given to kerosene, a liquid.

Paraffin oil
A confusing term.

Kerosene in the USA is called *paraffin* in the UK whereas *liquid paraffin* in the UK equates to *mineral oil* (q.v.) in the USA. UK-variety *liquid paraffin* is sticky stuff and will not burn in a kerosene lamp.

Bottled lamp fuel in the USA is sometimes labeled *paraffin oil*. I've always thought that the seller was implying his product was odorless (a kind of liquefied paraffin canning wax, if you will) and not smelly (like kerosene). In practice, the term *paraffin oil* seems to be a marketing term and means whatever the seller wants it to mean. Buyer beware.

Paulin
A brand of wall-mounted mantle-lamp burning natural gas.

Petrol
The British name for gasoline.

Petroleum
(1) In the USA, petroleum is nearly synonymous with crude oil ("petroleum products").
(2) "Petroleum" in German has a narrower meaning and translates as kerosene in English.

ppm
Acronym for parts per million.

Propane
C_3H_8 A refinery gas; a petroleum product. Ethane has two carbon atoms. Propane has three. Butane has four.

q.v.
Abbreviation for Latin *quod vide* meaning "which see."

Ronson
A brand of cigarette lighter.

Ronsonal
A brand of cigarette lighter fuel.

sic
Used in written text to indicate that a quote is not a mistake or a typographical error. Rather, the quote is to be read as it stands. Colloquially, *sic* means, "That's the way I got it, folks."

Spontaneous combustion
". . . the ignition of bodies by the internal development of heat without the application of an external flame. It not infrequently takes place among heaps of rags . . . lubricated with oil . . ." – *Encyclopedia Americana, 1919*

Stoddard solvent
Mineral spirits (q.v.).

Sulfur
The element sulfur causes the strong smell of diesel fuel, kerosene, and the like.

TEOTWAWKI
An acronym for The End Of The World As We Know It.

Ultra-Pure
A brand of synthetic fuel, a kerosene substitute, boasting low odor.

Unleaded gas
In the beginning, gasoline from the refinery (white gas) had no additives and an octane rating of 50. Autos evolved that needed higher octane. Tetraethyl lead was an additive that raised the octane level. Lead poisoned people, however, and leaded gas was replaced, by law, with unleaded. But "unleaded" does not mean "no additives." No additives would translate to 50 octane.

Vaseline
A trademark for a petroleum jelly (a.k.a. petrolatum).

VM&P naphtha
Varnish makers' and painters' naphtha.

Wax

A solid, greasy, heat-sensitive substance that serves as fuel in a candle.

White gas
Clear, 50-octane gas with no additives.

White spirits
Stoddard solvent or mineral spirits.

Zippo
A brand of cigarette lighter. Also a brand of fuel for cigarette lighters.